REAL-WORLD LEARNING

PREPARING FOR YOUR PROFESSION OUTSIDE OF THE CLASSROOM

FIRST EDITION

By Bernadette Friedrich
Michigan State University

cognella® | ACADEMIC PUBLISHING

Bassim Hamadeh, CEO and Publisher
Michael Simpson, Vice President of Acquisitions
Jamie Giganti, Senior Managing Editor
Miguel Macias, Graphic Designer
Amy Stone, Field Acquisitions Editor
Mirasol Enriquez, Senior Project Editor
Luiz Ferreira, Senior Licensing Specialist

First published in the United States of America in 2017 by Cognella, Inc.

Cover image copyright © Depositphotos/Rawpixel.

Printed in the United States of America

ISBN: 978-1-63487-500-4 (pbk) / 978-1-63487-501-1 (br)

Table of Contents

Chapter 3

Mindfulness Mind-set   20

Chapter 4

Exploring Professional Opportunities—Experience Industry vs. Academics   30

Chapter 5

Expectations—What you think you know about work! 40

Chapter 6

Professional Ethics—Is it right or wrong?   50

Chapter 7

Professionalism and Workplace Relationships — 60

Chapter 8

Communications—What is everyone talking about? — 70

Chapter 9

Why do I need to understand economics? I have no budget. — 80

Chapter 10

I have managed my life, I can manage a project!   88

Chapter 11

Yeah, what is this whole work-life balance thing?   98

Chapter 12

Make it so! Your future looks bright!   **106**

For the things we have to learn before we can do them, we learn by doing them.

—Aristotle, The Nicomachean Ethics

How to use this workbook

Each chapter is designed around a specific career-related or career-development topic. Information is included in each chapter that provides you with a theoretical basis for the exploration as well as practical understanding and application of the knowledge you will develop. In addition, each chapter ends with a worksheet. Worksheets have been developed and provided for you to explore each topic and how it relates to your future career.

These worksheets are designed for you, not your faculty advisor, your supervisor, or your mother. Take them seriously and personally! I honestly believe that by applying the same problem-solving principles you apply in your major courses to these worksheets, you will be well prepared for a satisfying career post-graduation. You will be consciously exploring concepts that most people just stumble upon somewhere between years 5 and 10 of their careers.

Many of the worksheets will require you to develop a learning objective or two. This is an opportunity for you to determine what it is you want to get out of the chapter specifically, but more importantly, the work experience as a whole. I want to take a few minutes to assist you in understanding what a learning objective is, how to write one, and how to measure your progress.

So, what is a learning objective? "A learning objective is an outcome statement that captures specifically what knowledge, skills, and attitudes learners should be able to exhibit following instruction."* Yeah, okay, so what does that really mean? As a student you have been inundated with information. Frankly, as a faculty member, I know you are not going to retain all of it. Frankly, as a student, I know I would not care to retain it all. But I do care, and you will want to at least get something out of your experience that is meaningful to you. I am under no illusion that many of you think this type of course is busywork. In my opinion, this may be the most important course you are taking. But you aren't going to remember it all, and some topics you are going to skim over, so the purpose of the learning objective is to help you figure out what you really do want to get out of the course. So work with me here!

A few simple rules about objectives, goals, outcomes:

> **Specific**—You know, not vague
> **Measurable**—Quantifiable
> **Achievable**—Let's be realistic here
> **Relevant**—As my advisor used to say, "Who cares?"
> **Targeted**—I don't expect you to ask yourself to do something that is outside the realm of your expertise or interest

Let's take a simple topic: Learning the alphabet

As a teacher, I say that I am going to provide you with all the letters of the alphabet in an orderly manner. I am going to show you the actual symbol, demonstrate the pronunciation, and provide examples of usage in a word (real-world application).

As a student, what do you want to get out of the lesson?

As a student, I want to be able to recognize and recite the letters of the alphabet in sequence and within common words by the end of this month. Simple, right? (Note the words *recognize* and *recite*, instead of *learn* and *know*.)

Okay, let's practice something more conducive to your intellectual ability. Take a look at the syllabus from one of your major courses. At the beginning of your syllabus, objectives are named.

The key concepts and related content your professor wants you to learn are listed in these objectives. As you go through the major curriculum you will see some of these objectives repeated in a variety of courses. They will probably address things such as communication; understanding the worldview and how it relates to your major and professional ethics; specific skill sets like problem solving and critical thinking; and include some social issues, like working in a diverse environment and being a productive team member. In addition, the objectives will be specific to the course content: fluid dynamics, accounting, psychology.

All of that is pretty esoteric, so you tell me, what do you want to get out of college?

As a student I will be able to

_____

_____

Read that over! Now how did you do? Tell me, specifically please! Is it

Specific?   _____

Measurable? _____

Achievable? _____

Realistic?   _____

Targeted?   _____

So here is a solid example:

By the end of this semester I will be able to demonstrate my understanding of basic material properties by identifying chemical properties based on the structure of atoms, molecules, and ions.

Note that this objective highlights just one part of the learning process. Don't try to lump everything into one learning objective.

Other assignments give you the specific tasks related to the topic of the chapter. These assignments are to help you further understand the concepts and learn to apply them to your reality!

*"Effective Use of Performance Objectives for Learning and Assessment." *The University of New Mexico School of Medicine. 2015. Fid.medicin.arizona.edu/ sites/default/files/u4/writingmeasurableobjectives_unm.pdf*

Chapter 1

Introduction to Your Profession

Student Objectives

- Understand the variety and breadth of their academic discipline
- Develop an awareness of professional employment opportunities most commonly associated with their field of study
- Begin to identify areas of interest and professional career focus

To provide simple scientific solutions to complex design problems is the job of an engineer.

—Bhupesh B. Patil

First we must understand the difference between a job title and a major, and then we can explore the many variations and paths to a more focused career trajectory. A job or position title usually describes the job level (manager, chief), the responsibilities (supervise, test), the functional area of the position (engineering, accounting), or the actual tasks involved in the position (coordinate, program). A major is an area of study at the collegiate level, a focused series of courses that provide the student with an in-depth understanding of a particular discipline, such as mechanical engineering, marketing, psychology, agricultural economics. In most cases students take courses to prepare them for the field, (i.e., are major-specific) as well as courses that provide a more well-rounded perspective on the world: history, communication, social science. At the end of this chapter you will explore this topic as it relates to your major.

Choosing a major is an important step in the life of a young adult. There are many careers where your college major or even a college degree may have little or no impact on propelling you in the right direction; for example, an auctioneer/auction house manager, chef, or professional athlete. On the other hand, some careers require very specialized educational paths; for example, nursing, medicine, engineering, accounting. It is important for you to understand that there may be a very specific educational path to your chosen career, but it's just as important to know that you are going to learn an abundance of skills in any curriculum that can be transferred to a variety of professions. For example, individuals with engineering degrees have become successful astronauts, actors, United States presidents, medical doctors, lawyers, head coaches in the National Football League, famous musicians, and cartoonists. In the same vein, people outside of a particular discipline are credited with some amazing discoveries. Was Ben Franklin a statesman or an inventor? Was Carl Jung a journalist or a social scientist? Was Jane Goodall an animal rights activist or an anthropologist?

Liz Freedman tells us that "choosing a major is a choice that should be intentional and based on knowledge of one's self...." [1] I don't know about you, but when I was 18 I wasn't really sure who I was, let alone who I wanted to be. Not to mention that your major, your area of technical expertise or subject knowledge, is only one part of what it means to be happy and successful in the world of work. There is a lot of talk these days about the "T-shaped" professional, with the stem of the T being a deep knowledge of and understanding about your specific discipline: mechanical engineering, finance, mathematics, etc. The cross of the T is the ability to understand and communicate within a broad variety of disciplines. For example, as an engineer you are hopefully an expert in your discipline, but as a professional you also need the skill set to interact on a multidisciplinary team, to communicate effectively to those outside of the discipline, to be able to connect across cultures, and so forth.

You are going to end up somewhere... why not begin to figure that out while you have the opportunity to really explore and not wait until you just need a job to pay the bills and be an adult? I am hoping that through this course you will solidify your understanding of your profession, eliminate some of the professional options that are currently still available to you, and identify some of the broader skills that you will need to master in order to be the best professional that you can be.

Real-Life Examples

Let's talk about some people who are successful, who started out in a particular field, and who can be classified as a developed T-shaped professional.

Jimmy Carter	President of the United States, peanut farmer, diplomat, engineer
Hedy Lamarr	Actress, spy, electronics patent holder
Alfred Hitchcock	Writer, producer, special effects master, engineer
Brian May	Guitarist (Queen), songwriter, audio enthusiast, astrophysicist (PhD)
Montel Williams	Talk show host/TV personality, fluent speaker of Mandarin, navy officer, engineer

Now how about some we know of because of their work in engineering:

Nikola Tesla	Engineer, inventor
Orville and Wilbur Wright	Flying enthusiasts, aerodynamics engineers
Archimedes	Mathematician, astronomer, physicist, engineer
Thomas Edison	Businessman, inventor, electrical engineer
Leonardo da Vinci	Inventor, artist, engineer
Nicolaus Copernicus	Religious figure, astronomer, scholar, scientist

Alfred Nobel	Business leader, inventor, scientist
Carl Jung	Journalist, psychologist
Charles Henry Turner	Educator, zoologist, scientist
Linda B. Buck	Biologist

Activity(ies)

Pick one of the above individuals (Real-Life Examples) and tell me why you think they are T-shaped as you understand the concept.

Look at your own education, experience, and activities and tell me how you are developing skills across the T.

Identify a person who had a degree in your discipline and yet succeeded in a nontraditional role. Explore their path to success and indicate whether and how you think their field of study helped them get there.

Identify and interview a person who has been successful in your field of study. What did their education look like? How did they get to their current position? What decisions did they have to make along the way? How did they make those decisions?

Summary

As you can see, most majors are part of a very broad discipline. In modern society it almost always means that the individual has a college education with very specific training related to a particular discipline. Those disciplines can be broad like electrical engineering, business management, or psychology. Or they can be very specific like automotive engineering, accounting, child psychology. In many cases, once you enter the workforce your major will be much less significant than your position title. Examples of titles: process engineer, design engineer, account manager, office manager, counselor, caseworker, business analyst.

Your major will teach you the principles of your discipline, in addition to specifics related to the major, but the job that you eventually achieve will take your skill set, your personality, your career goals, your work–life balance needs, and many other factors into account. For most of us it is a matter of trial and error to determine where exactly we want to be in the professional world, and in fact, those goals can change as we grow personally and professionally. The purpose of this course is to get you started in that process of discovering where you want to initiate your professional career.

Keywords

Career goals

Profession

T-shaped professional

Suggested Readings

William Kamkwamba, *The Boy Who Harnessed the Wind*

Endnotes

1. Freedman, Liz. College Employment Research Institute. *Michigan State University.* 2015. www.ceri.msu.edu/t-shaped-professionals

1. Create a learning objective related to learning about your profession.

    _____

    _____

    _____

    _____

2. Describe at least three steps you will take to achieve this objective.

    _____

    _____

    _____

    _____

3. Why is this objective important to you?

    _____

    _____

    _____

    _____

4. Learning objective check-up:

2 weeks _____   Update

4 weeks _____   Update

8 weeks _____   Update

12 weeks _____   Update

5. Did you completely achieve this goal? If so how? If not, what still needs to be done?

_____
_____
_____
_____

Chapter 2

Lifelong Learning

Isn't that something that happens after you graduate from college?

Student Objectives

- Understand the concept of lifelong learning and how it applies to them
- Be able to identify individuals and resources for lifelong learning opportunities
- Develop a bucket list of lifelong learning topics

Anyone who stops learning is old, whether at twenty or eighty. Anyone who keeps learning stays young.

—Henry Ford

The purpose of this chapter is to provide you with a road map that you will use the rest of your life to enhance your learning and continued growth. We have trained you as students to learn what we are telling you to learn, whether it is memorizing vocabulary and times tables in third grade or using theorems and equations to solve complex mathematical problems. The reality is, yes, we want you to know how to perform these tasks and communicate effectively. But more importantly we want you to be able to solve problems based on the skill sets that you have, and know what skills you need to develop in order to continue to grow personally and professionally. This chapter will provide you with the basics for that lifelong learning.

"Lifelong learning" is a term that you may have heard, and sort of makes sense, but what are we actually talking about? Are we talking about formal education throughout our life? How about informal education, on-the-job training, personal interests? Do we mean the skill set we need to keep competitive in the workforce? Or the skills, knowledge, and ability to be a successful, contributing member to society? Well, depending on who you talk to, you are going to get a different answer. But let's look at some of the research; Aspin and Chapman[2] observed that institutions, governments, and societies are looking at the concept of lifelong learning and developing policies, practices, and intentions for educating citizens to create a strong groundwork for society. Obviously people have different opinions of the meaning and purpose of lifelong education, including preparing you for your adult life,[3] learning throughout your lifetime,[4] or learning from the entirety of one's life experiences.[5] In a practical sense, lifelong learning is a combination of all these things; many times it is probably an unconscious process, both the learning and the application of the learning in your life. The point is you can make a conscious effort to continue to learn, both as a professional and a contributing member of society.

But not all the answers are in the books. There is so much growth in technology, rapid changes in global commerce, deviations in geopolitics, and hundreds of unknown factors that will shape your future as a professional. Lifelong learning is what you will need to keep up with the changes. Think of your grandparents' and great-grandparents' use and understanding of technology, and compare that to your own. How will you learn to keep up? What will you need to learn to be a contributing member of society? What will you need to be on top of your game professionally? What did you not learn in school that you need to know to move into the career that you desire? All of these things are part of the process of lifelong learning.

Real-Life Examples

Do you remember when you first played a video game? Was it on Nintendo, Wii, a computer? How did you know how to play? Did you watch your friends? Did you read the instructions? Did you ask someone to show you? How do you think your parents learned to play video games? Do they even play? What types of games are they likely to play on their phone?

Do they even have games on their phone? How about when you first played soccer or basketball? Did your parents sign you up for an after-school league that taught you the basic moves, rules, and procedures? Or did you just play down the block with a bunch of neighbor kids?

Now let's think about your parents at work. Are they college educated? What did they study? Is that related to their current position? If they didn't go to college, how did they learn to do the job they are in? Whether you are a heart surgeon or a waitress, you had to learn how to do your job. Some professions obviously require a little more formal training and maybe even a license to practice, but the process of learning the skills to achieve, maintain, and advance in your profession remains the same: Lifelong learning!

Activity(ies)

Create a list of things that you would like to learn. Many of you have a bucket list, or at least have thought about something you might put on yours. List ten to fifteen things that you would like to learn in the near or distant future. The list can show languages, skills, games, etc.

Challenge your assumptions! Are you afraid to go to a certain city because you have heard bad things about it? Go and see what the city really has to offer.

If you have never attended a certain sports event because "that can't be any fun," seek one out. I think of fishing... I mean how exciting could a fishing competition be? You might just be surprised.

Go see a movie that you have no desire to see. Were you more entertained than you thought?

Think you aren't artistic? Take an art class; lots of opportunities are out there in community education programs or local businesses. If the first class doesn't work for you, try something else, from painting to ceramics to glass fusing. There are a ton of options to be explored.

Summary

Unfortunately in the fast pace of the world we live in, it is often only the necessary that is learned. It is important to learn what you need to do to be a good parent, a productive employee, and a contributing member to society. So beyond the activities in this course, and those things that you "have" to learn, seek learning outside of the obvious. We live in a society where working hard is not the only way to get ahead. You have to work smart, be on top of the knowledge network that currently drives and will continue to drive our society and the global economy. There may even be instances within your discipline that your bachelor's degree doesn't satisfy the minimum formal education required for you to be a practicing professional. Those individuals who will be ahead in the game are those who continue to learn and can articulate that learning to a potential employer for a job, or their supervisor for a raise or a promotion. Take advantage of all learning that is available to you, whether formal, informal, organizational, or independent.

In reality, lifelong learning is a process that for many of you will occur naturally. Whether it is learning to be a parent, an employee, or a business owner, you will continue to learn throughout your life. But these are obvious; I would encourage you to challenge yourself to learn things that aren't a "natural" progression of your life.

Keywords

Lifelong learning

Process

Formal education

Informal education

Organizational learning

Endnotes

2. Aspin, D.N. & Chapman, J.D. "Lifelong Learning: Concepts and Conceptions." *International Journal of Lifelong Education, 19* (1), 2–19, 2000.

3. White, J.P. *The Aims of Education Restated.* London: Croom Helm, 1982.

4. Kulich, J. "Lifelong Learning and the Universities: A Canadian Perspective." *International Journal of Lifelong Education.* (2), 123–142.

5. Pena-Borrero, M. "Lifelong Education and Social Change." *International Journal of Lifelong Education, 3(1)*: 1–15.

1. What are some areas of lifelong learning that you think you will need to remain competitive in
   a. your particular field?
   b. the workplace in general?
   c. your personal life?

2. Identify resources for lifelong learning:

   _____

   _____

   _____

   _____

3. Describe at least three steps you will take to achieve this objective.

   _____

   _____

   _____

   _____

4. Why is this objective important to you?

_____

_____

_____

_____

5. Learning objective check-up:

2 weeks _____   Update

4 weeks _____   Update

8 weeks _____   Update

12 weeks _____   Update

6. Did you completely achieve this goal? If so how? If not, what still needs to be done?

_____

_____

_____

_____

Chapter 3

Mindfulness Mind-set

- Become aware of their own frame of mind
- Learn if they are open to new things or tend to stick with the known
- Understand how their mindfulness/mind-set will impact their decision making and choices

Reflection and action must never be undertaken independently.

—Paulo Friere

Sometimes we go through life without thinking! Seriously, we make choices, often thinking we are considering all the factors, but are we? So what exactly do I mean, "mindfulness and mind-set"? Are we going on a journey of meditation? Is yoga in your future? Well, not precisely. Instead we are going to look at how you approach information, problems, and circumstances. Let's call it yoga of the mind!

Anyone ever tell you that you have a bad attitude? (Think teacher, coach, parent.) How about the opposite? Anyone ever say to you that you have such a positive approach to something? Or how they are amazed at how you deal with setbacks, problems? Would you consider yourself an optimist, pessimist, or realist? We will explore these ideas and how knowing where you are can help you be more successful in dealing with the good, the bad, and the ugly!

First, let's define mindfulness. According to the Merriam-Webster Dictionary, mindfulness is the "state or quality of being mindful; inclined to be aware."[6] A more academic definition is the "technique in which one focuses one's full attention only on the present, experiencing thoughts, feelings, and sensations but not judging them."[7]

Basically, this is the concept of being conscious of how you are feeling about something that is present right now. Ever had one of those moments when you thought, Wow, this is really a beautiful day! The sun is shining, a light breeze, everything is so green. Or how about recognizing something about yourself? Ugh, I am so frustrated with this homework. I don't understand why I can't grasp these concepts. This is the act of being mindful, aware of your feelings and being present in the moment.

Another concept we need to understand is mind-set. Again with the online dictionary: Mind-set is "an attitude, disposition or mood."[8] In my examples of mindfulness I hinted at the *mind-set* in the moment? Can you guess what they are? In the first example, I am joyful, happy, impressed with the day! But in the second, I am not so happy; my mind-set is more negative.

Think of the people in your life. Do you have what I refer to as a "Doubting Dan" or a "Debbie Downer"? How about a "Positive Polly"? I am sure that you can recognize those who are more optimistic than pessimistic and vice versa. Can you recognize that in yourself? We are going to explore that a little more deeply in this chapter. But the real question here is why it matters. Well, I am glad you asked. Carol Dweck's[7] research suggests that it matters a lot. That those with a more positive mind-set approach life differently and in general have a more positive as well as a more successful experience.

As humans we are great about creating and sticking with routines. We like a level of comfort; we develop habits, favorite resources for information. We go through life without thinking; well at least without thinking about how we are feeling, what kind of attitude we have toward something. I know you don't really believe this, so let me give you an example. Did you ever wake up and say, "I really just don't want to go to class today"? Was it because you just didn't feel like it? Was it because you had a big homework assignment that you hadn't completed? Was it because you tripped over your backpack when getting ready to leave?

The first one, I just didn't feel like it, is the one that provides us with the best example of mindfulness. Why don't you feel like it? I mean the homework assignment, that could be fear, disappointment, frustration. The backpack, pure embarrassment! But "I just didn't feel like it." There is a root cause, and hopefully by the end of this chapter and course, you will have a better idea of why it is important to know why you just didn't feel like it, and how to change that mind-set for the better.

Real-Life Examples

I would like to name some people and see if you can tell me where their mind-set might be.

Helen Keller

Bill Gates

Bethany Hamilton

Oprah Winfrey

Thomas Edison

Lindsay Lohan

Anne Frank

Stieg Larsson

Okay so we all know that Helen Keller had some real obstacles in her life in dealing with both vision and hearing disabilities. Helen went on to accomplish more things than most physically capable people do. Maybe more significantly, as a woman, Helen had to grapple with many gender barriers that someone in your generation wouldn't even begin understand, let alone face. Helen was the first deaf and blind person to receive a bachelor's degree; she was a renowned author, speaker, and political activist. To me her understanding of mindfulness and her mind-set are both summed up in this one quote: "When one door of happiness closes, another opens; but often we look so long at the closed door that we do not see the one which has been opened for us."[9] What does that statement say to you?

What do you know of these other people? What is your first impression of their mind-set? You are aware that many of these individuals have faced external hardships and some have faced internal hardships. Some were not known until after their death, and you may not even recognize some of them. What impact might mind-set have on success in life, or lack of success?

Think of people you know, those who are already in their post-education careers, those who you are currently studying with, and maybe some in your social circle. Can you identify those whom you think will have a high degree of success? What mindful characteristics do they exhibit?

Activity(ies)

Pick two of the people from the list above, one you are familiar with and one you are not. Do a little research and write a brief paragraph on what you might imagine with their mind-set to be. How did that affect their lives?

Take the following quiz. What do the results tell you about your mind-set? http://www.quizony.com/are-you-an-optimist-pessimist-or-realist/index.html

By trying this exercise, you can become conscious of your own mindfulness. Set an alarm on your phone to go off sometime in the next week, preferably a time you know you will be awake. When the alarm goes off, take a few minutes to recognize first what you are doing: driving home from work, playing tennis with a friend, working on the computer? Next identify how you are feeling: competitive, anxious, frustrated, calm, content? Are you giving this one activity your full attention, or are you worrying about work while you play tennis, are you thinking about meeting friends while you are working on your project? Repeat this exercise several times over the next month. If you think of it at random times, engage the process then. Being in the present will make you a more efficient and effective participant in that activity.

Summary

So going back to what your Mom said to you a long time ago, "Attitude matters." You aren't always going to love everything you do, you aren't going to find a thrill in every challenge, but looking forward to life instead of dreading it is going to make you much more likely to succeed in the little things and therefore succeed in the bigger things.

Keywords

Mind-set

Mindfulness

Supporting Materials

- TedTalk. A Growth Mind-set for a Creative Mind https://www.youtube.com/watch?v=y-ia-CWBHFU
- Dr. Amar G. Bose. Last Lecture of Fall '96 Acoustics Course (starting at 54:00/1:01) http://video.mit.edu/watch/dr-amar-g-bose-last-lecture-of-fall-96-acoustics-course-6698/
- Langer, E.J. (1997). *The Power of Mindful Learning*. Cambridge, MA: Perseus Books.

- TedTalk. Angela Lee Duckworth on Grit http://www.ted.com/talks/
  angela_lee_duckworth_the_key_to_success_grit#t-36602

Endnotes

6. "Mindful." *Merriam-Webster.com*. Merriam-Webster, n.d. Web. 28 June 2015. <http://
   www.merriam-webster.com/dictionary/mindful>.

7. "Mindfulness." Dictionary.com. *Dictionary.com Unabridged*. Random House, Inc.
   http://dictionary.reference.com/browse/mindfulness (accessed: June 28, 2015).

8. "Mind-set." Dictionary.com. *Dictionary.com Unabridged*. Random House, Inc. http://
   dictionary.reference.com/browse/mindset (accessed: June 28, 2015).

9. Dweck, C.S. 2006. *Mind-set: The New Psychology of Success*. New York: Random
   House.

10. Keller, Helen. www.quotationspage.com/quote/30190.html (accessed: June 28, 2015).

1. Create a goal regarding your own mindfulness or mind-set.

   _____

   _____

   _____

   _____

2. Describe at least three steps you will take to achieve this goal.

   _____

   _____

   _____

   _____

3. Why is this goal important to you?

   _____

   _____

   _____

   _____

4. Goal check-up:

    2 weeks _____   Update

    4 weeks _____   Update

    8 weeks _____   Update

    12 weeks _____   Update

5. Did you completely achieve this goal? If so, how? If not, what still needs to be done?

_____

_____

_____

_____

Chapter 4

Exploring Professional Opportunities

Experience Industry vs. Academics

Student Objectives

- Broaden their understanding of their field of study, and that of their particular discipline
- Begin to identify their likes and dislikes in relation to career opportunities
- Learn how different experiences provide the basis for achieving their ultimate career goals

Life is not only about acquiring knowledge, it is about applying knowledge.

—Amit Kalantri

Some students think engineers and accountants are very marketable, and can obtain a good job after graduation relatively easily in the current market. But ideally the student will end their college career having a more defined professional focus and the skill set to obtain the position that is most closely related to their goals and values.

So you want to be a _____ (Fill in the blank with your chosen profession)!

Great, now what do you want to do? No really, what do you want to do? In the first chapter we talked about the various majors and also about job titles. There are thousands of career options for those with a college degree. First, there are the obvious ones, usually containing the "major"; for example: manufacturing engineering, cost accountant, financial manager. But the other possibilities are endless: lawyer, physician, politician, entrepreneur, architect, musician, … . We discussed famous people who either had specific degrees or basically functioned within a discipline in their own time, but were they the exception to the rule or are college majors really that versatile? In this chapter, we will explore and hopefully provide some insight into that question.

Can you name a profession where individuals practice in the workplace before finishing their undergraduate education? How about nursing? Teaching? Counseling? There has been extensive research to indicate that exploring your chosen field of study prior to graduation is the most effective and efficient method for understanding the potential of your career path.[10] Research also suggests that those who participate in professionally related work while still in school are more successful students and rise faster in the professional world post-graduation.[11]

I have often told students if you go out on a co-op assignment, then come back to school and tell me you don't want to be an engineer, I consider that a success. Much better to find it out while they are still a student and can redirect their education to something that is more suited to what they want to do. Even if a student doesn't change their major, they can confirm a career path or even narrow down their professional options for post-graduation work.

If you thought choosing a college was hard, and choosing your major was hard, and you know that those are only going to define you for four or five or six years of your life, imagine how hard it must be to choose a career path. I occasionally get a student in my office who is distressed because they don't know that they want to do "engineering" the rest of their life. "Doing engineering" is an image they have created from their experiences about what an engineer must do day in and day out. In ninety percent of the cases, they haven't even observed an engineer at work, let alone more than one to even have an inkling of what an engineer might do. This is true for students in all majors, even those which seem pretty obvious like nursing and teaching. The fields are as varied as there are stars in the sky!

Real-Life Examples

Bill Gates

Mayim Bialik

Gene Simmons

Francis Bacon

Chester Carlson

Shaquille O'Neal

Kris Kristofferson

Edith Clarke

Martha J. Coston

Activity(ies)

Tell me about why you decided to become an accountant, engineer, social worker. What did you see yourself doing on a daily basis?

As a child or teen, did you work on your own vehicle, build your own computer, create chemical experiments in your backyard (or in the kitchen)? Did you play store or business, teach the other kids in your classroom, hang up a sign for counseling à la Lucy from *Peanuts*?

Choose two of the people from the list above and learn about their professional career paths. What do you find significant in their route to their current (or most recent) position? Have you thought of doing anything similar? What do you think their original career goals were? What may have influenced their choices? Think about the times they live or lived in and or other special skills they may have exhibited.

Using the Internet or other resource, find three or four job descriptions for the job that you think you want after graduation. Are the descriptions the same? Are they different?

Again, searching your school's webpage, find the CV of three or four of your favorite professors. What things have they reported being involved in during their career? Interview one or two and ask them if they have had other work experience prior to academia, even as a young adult. Also ask them why they chose to teach instead of working in industry.

Write a list of pros and cons of working in industry and working in academia. After reviewing the lists, what excites you about each career path? What is keeping you from exploring one or the other?

Summary

There is no single right choice when deciding your career path. As you talk to more and more professionals you meet along the way, you will learn that many took a very circuitous path to their current position. It may have begun with changing majors as a college student or not finding satisfaction in their first job out of school. Everyone should have a plan, but don't be so stuck to the plan that you ignore opportunities that are offered to you. It may be an internship in a field or company that you hadn't previously found interesting. It may be taking a course in a field that is completely outside of your planned educational path. It may be taking a semester or even a couple of weeks to travel to states, countries, or continents that you haven't previously visited. It could also be just joining a campus club outside of your major. You never know where your road will take you!

Keywords

Academia

Industry

Professor

CV or Curricula Vitae

Suggested Readings

http://phdcomics.com/comics.php

The Professor Is In: The Essential Guide to Turning Your Ph.D. into a Job

by Karen Kelsky

The PhD Movie

Endnotes

10. Heinemann, H.N., DeFalco, A. & Smelkinson, M. (1992). "Work-Experience Enriched Learning." *The Journal of Cooperative Education*, 23(1), 65–67.

11. Hadara, M., Skanes, H. (2007). "Strengthening Academic Ties by Assessment of Learning Outcomes." *The Journal of Cooperative Education*, 35(1): 41–47.

1. Attempt to narrow down your top ten job choices upon graduation. Is continued education a part of this? If so, include that in the following discussion.

   _____

   _____

   _____

   _____

2. Describe at least three steps you will take to achieve this objective.

   _____

   _____

   _____

   _____

3. What characteristics did you take into account when determining your choices?

   _____

   _____

   _____

   _____

4. How will you go about making yourself ready for these options?

_____

_____

_____

_____

5. Have you changed your mind about any of these goals three months later?

_____

_____

_____

_____

Chapter 5

Expectations

What you think you know about work!

Student Objectives

- Be able to articulate their expectations of both the co-op/ intern work experience and full-time employment
- Understand the university's expectations of the student and the employer
- Explore the employer's expectations of the student, the work, and the intern program
- Be able to balance all of these expectations with their own in a meaningful way

My expectations were reduced to zero when I was 21. Everything since then has been a bonus.

—Stephen Hawking

Our expectations of an event or activity influence the mental state we have going into the activity. But more importantly, our expectations can influence our response during and after the activity. Having unrealistic expectations can cloud the experience and influence your perception of the opportunity.

Do you remember as a child being all excited about the first day of school? Your first vacation? Your best friend's birthday party? I am sure your parents told you how fun school was going to be and you were going to make friends and learn a lot of things. We all had something that we were looking forward to for one reason or another. How did reality match up with those expectations? For the most successful workplace experience, it is important that your expectations of the experience match as closely as possible to the expectations of your school and your employer.

There is an extensive amount of research done on expectations, including those of the workplace, new employees, trainees, and perceived outcomes.[12–16] What these researchers want to know is how people develop expectations and whether those expectations have an influence on the success of the employment

41

experience. Satisfaction with an experience is most certainly based on what we are anticipating. Think about what you have been told about doing an internship. How has that shaped your expectations? Think about what you have heard about being an engineer. How has that shaped your expectations? Think about the coursework that you have participated in. How has that shaped your expectations?

The same research also tells us that those who have realistic expectations of any event are more likely to report a positive outcome of the experience. It is extremely important to develop realistic expectations through exploration. If you can learn to do it now, while in school and prior to looking for a full-time position, you will begin to form the skill set you need to to align your expectations of employment with what the employer is offering, both in tasks and professional growth. You have heard of self-fulfilling prophecy. The concept that if you think something is going to happen, you will make choices for that event to happen. Usually made in reference to negative events, but you get the point. Your expectations impact your experience! By the end of this chapter, you will better understand the expectations of the employer and of your educational institution. You will be able to create realistic expectations of your experiential education, whether it be an internship, a cooperative education experience, or an undergraduate research experience.

Real-Life Examples

Student A, Kris: An academically successful senior has a 3.8 GPA with just one semester until graduation. Kris is a member of several student groups, but has held no elected or leadership positions. Kris has heard other students talking about how important an internship is for post-graduation employment opportunities, but Kris is confident that a strong GPA will be enough for getting a job after graduation.

Student B, Pat: A raising junior with a 2.9 GPA has been actively involved with several student groups, including being vice-president of ASME and a representative on the Student Engineering Council. Pat is concerned about obtaining an internship based on a sub-par GPA. Pat realizes that some pre-graduation work experience is essential to post-graduation employment success.

Student C, Lynn: A freshman accounting student is required by the first-year business program to attend a career fair. Lynn has no business courses completed, is taking Calculus I, and has work experience only in mowing lawns for neighbors. Knowing points for the final grade will be awarded for attending the fair, Lynn created a résumé in the course and provides it to employers at the event. .

Activity(ies)

Each of these students is a familiar face in our office. Which one do you most identify with? How do you think each of them will fare at the career event? What advice would you give each of them and why?

Create of list of your expectations of your upcoming work experience. Include what you expect to do, what you expect to learn, what you expect to contribute. Create a list of what you imagine the expectations of the employer are for your upcoming work experience. Include what they expect from you, what they expect you to know, what they expect you to contribute.

Create a list of what you imagine the expectations of your educational institution are for your work experience. What is the school expecting from the employer? What are they expecting from you? Compare these three lists. Where is there agreement? Where is there disagreement? Why do you think there is a discrepancy? What steps would you take to resolve these inconsistencies in expectations? If there are no discrepancies, why do you think that is?

Of all of these expectations, which one are you most excited about? If these expectations are not met, how do you think you will perform on the job? How will you view your overall experience at the end of the placement?

Summary

It is very important to remember that expectations exist on both sides of the relationship. Your employer will also have expectations of you, and if you are not living up to those expectations, that might also create friction within the employee–employer relationship. For example, you are offered a position and told that you would be involved in product design and would be working at headquarters in medium-sized city in the Midwest. You eagerly accept the position, but within four months after you accepted the offer and before you were to start, you're notified that particular project has been canceled. The company says you can stay in that city and work on another project (which doesn't sound like anything you would want to do) or you can take a position in a rural outpost working on a similar project.

I recently had a situation where a young electrical engineering student was hired at a power company for a cooperative education experience. Let's call this student Brandy. Brandy had a great first semester with the company and was looking forward to returning for her second rotation. However, while in school, she determined that she was more interested in a degree in biomedical engineering. She switched her major and is so far very satisfied with her choice. Upon returning to the power company, Brandy met with the human resources officer who, after reviewing Brandy's academic program, told her that she would most likely not be offered a full-time position with the power company. Brandy was very upset—she thought she had done a great job with the company, and indeed she had. But the employer expectation was that they were hiring a student in electrical engineering; a student they felt had a particular interest in and knowledge of the power company. Brandy, on the other hand, thought that she had done a good job with her given tasks and therefore would be offered a full-time position upon graduation. Clearly the expectations of the two sides are not congruent.

It is cases like Brandy's that are most distressing to students. I am sure that she will obtain a full-time position that is more in line with her ultimate career goals and in fact will be much more content with her full-time employment. If she had indeed received a position at the power company, she may have ended up frustrated and confused over her role within the organization.

Keywords

Expectations

Personal expectations

Professional expectations

Supporting Materials

Dont live down to expectations. Go out there and do something remarkable. - Wendy Wasserstein

Great achievements are the results of great expectations. You will see it happen only when you believe it will happen. - Unknown

Endnotes

12. Bigley, Gregory A., and Steers, Richard M. 2003. *Motivation and Work Behavior.* McGraw-Hill, Inc., New York.

13. Buckley, M. Ronald, Fedor, Donald B., Veres, John G., Wiese, Danielle S., and Carraher, Shawn M. "Investigating Newcomer Expectations and Job-Related Outcomes." *Journal of Applied Psychology* 83, no. 3 (1998): 452.

14. Gregory, Irving, P., and Meyer, John P. "Reexamination of the Met-Expectations Hypothesis: A Longitudinal Analysis." *Journal of Applied Psychology* 79, no. 6 (1994): 937.

15. Major, Debra A., Kozlowski, Steve W. J., Chao, Georgia T., and Gardner, Philip D. "A Longitudinal Investigation of Newcomer Expectations, Early Socialization Outcomes, and the Moderating Effects of Role Development Factors." *Journal of Applied Psychology* 80, no. 3 (1995): 418.

16. Tannenbaum, Scott I., Mathieu, John E., Salas, Eduardo, and Cannon-Bowers, Janis A. "Meeting Trainees' Expectations: The Influence of Training Fulfillment on the Development of Commitment, Self-Efficacy, and Motivation." *Journal of Applied Psychology* 76, no. 6 (1991): 759.

1. Create a list of three academic expectations that would be a real challenge.

_____

_____

_____

_____

2. Create a list of three professional expectations that would not challenge you at all.

_____

_____

_____

_____

3. What are the steps you would need to take to achieve the high expectations? Would you have to make compromises in other parts of your life? Are you willing to do that?

_____

_____

_____

_____

4. If you are aiming for only a low set of expectations, are there other things that you would spend your time on? Would those things assist you in obtaining the perfect post-graduation position? If so, how?

_____

_____

_____

_____

5. How, based on this worksheet, can you create realistic expectations?

_____

_____

_____

_____

6. Google quotes on expectations. Pick one that resonates with you. How does it make you feel?

_____

_____

_____

_____

7. Why do expectations matter?

_____

_____

_____

_____

Chapter 6

Professional Ethics

Is it right or wrong?

Student Objectives

- Understand workplace principles of integrity
- Locate, read, and understand the engineering professional of their discipline
- Identify and understand their value system
- Be able to identify an ethical situation and understand the method to resolve it

In just about every area of society, there's nothing more important than ethics.

—Henry Paulson

Did you ever look at a situation and wonder how individuals or organizations decide what is right and what is wrong? Obviously, sometimes you look at circumstances and know whether they are clearly wrong or clearly right, but more often you can look at a situation and see both sides and maybe even some ambiguity on the correct resolution. It is for this reason that most professional organizations have a code of ethics. These are guidelines created and supported by a governing body of the profession to help individuals navigate those gray areas. In this chapter, we will explore the development of ethics within the professional realm as well as general professional work principles.

Do you know where to find your professional ethics? Who determines workplace ethics and how do you know what is acceptable? Do you know what role you play in maintaining both professional and workplace ethics? Is there room for interpretation? Ethical situations can be a stressful time for new professionals. Although there are many standards and resources, new professionals don't always know where to go for the basics, nor do they know how to handle when a supervisor or customer is asking them to do something they think may be outside of the ethical standards.

Both ancient and modern philosophers have addressed the topics of ethics. Aristotle, an ancient Greek philosopher, says, "It is our choice of good or evil that determines our character, not our opinion about good or evil."[17] Harvey Mackay has a more direct thought, "Ethical decisions ensure that everyone's best interests are protected. When in doubt, don't."[18]

For all of human history, people have addressed the concept of doing what is right versus doing what is easy, most profitable, or better for the individual. The resolution is always the same: doing what is right is far better for both the human and humanity. A good friend of mine always uses a very simple phrase, "It doesn't look nice!" Like your parents and teachers have tried to instill in you, it is important to do the right thing.

So where do we start? I am guessing that you already have a good understanding of workplace ethics in general, even if you don't recognize it as such. Let's start with something simple. You are in college and at least at one point, you probably had a roommate. Your roommate had some really sweet headphones, headphones that you have wanted for a very long time. You are sitting in the study lounge and at one point, your roommate packs up his stuff and heads out to the library to meet some classmates. He forgets his headphones. Now as much as you would love to own those, you know that you don't and you pack them up with your things and leave them on his desk in the room. That is an ethical decision. Would it be illegal to steal them? Yes, but it would also be unethical. In this world there are a lot of things that may be legal, but not necessarily ethical. This can also be further convoluted by company policies. For example, it is not illegal to tell someone within the company your salary, but because some companies have a policy about disclosing your pay rate to others, many people feel disclosing pay rates is unethical.

I trust that most of you as educated individuals have a fairly good understanding of general personal ethics, and you can learn most workplace ethics by observation. In addition, many companies have a resource for determining ethical standards. This is where a supervisor, mentor, or human resources professional may provide you with the support that you need. What you may not be as familiar with, and what is more related to large financial and/or life-or-death situations, are those related to major workplace decisions. In general, professional codes of ethics are developed by a group of experienced professionals in the specific discipline and are based on situations or problems that have been presented to professional groups or individuals. Like any subset of society, rules, laws, ethical standards are developed and evolved in the attempt to solve existing problems and avoid future ones.

Real-Life Examples

The shuttle O-ring disaster
Mandated use of seat belts and airbags in passenger vehicles
Hurricane Katrina
The first artificial heart
The atomic bomb
Vaccinations
Enron
BP Oil Spill – Gulf of Mexico
Union Carbide – Bhopal
Lou Pearlman
Arthur Andersen
Beechnut
Starbucks

Activity(ies)

Choose an ethical situation above that is most closely related to your chosen major/career. After doing some research on the topic, explain what the ethical question was/is. Provide your insight into how you see the ethical decision making that happened in the development process and the use of the product. How do you feel about the decisions made before, during, and after? What impact did this issue have on ethics for future products? Is there a solid resolution to the ethical question?

Using the resources available to you, locate the code of ethics that is most closely related to your professional career/major. Was it easy to find? After reviewing the code, is there anything that surprises you? What and why?

Choose your current place of employment, or a company that you would like to work with and locate their company values. Was this easy to find? Is there anything there that surprises you? Are there any conflicts with your own values? With the professional code of ethics you identified above?

If you could add one item to either your professional code of ethics or your company's values, what would it be and why?

Summary

I am going on the assumption that most of you have been taught right from wrong your whole life! This came from a variety of sources: your parents, school and teachers, coaches, maybe some religious influence. You know there are rules in sports and school, you are aware that there are laws that dictate right and wrong in society. But as you enter the workforce, you will understand there are situations where the answer may not be so clear and that is when you turn to your profession's and company's codes of ethics or value statements. Understand that the answer is not always going to be clear. First, the question may be one that is affected differently by different ethnic or religious bodies. As discussed earlier, something could be legal, but is it ethical? Think about your process for determining if something is "right" or "wrong." Do not be afraid to discuss ethical choices and decisions with your classmates, group partners, or mentor.

Supporting Materials

https://drdianehamilton.wordpress.com/2011/12/15/8-important-business-ethics-cases/
A Short History of Ethics by Alasdair MacIntyre
Being Good by Simon Blackburn
Beyond Religion: Ethics for a Whole World by the Fourteenth Dalai Lama

Endnotes

17. Aristotle Quotes. "The European Graduate School." http://www.egs.edu/library/aristotle/quotes/ Accessed June 28, 2015.

18. Harvey Mackay Quotes. http://www.brainyquote.com/quotes/quotes/h/harveymack52876 Accessed June 28, 2015.

1. Become familiar with both your professional code of ethics
    and your company's value statement.

    _____

    _____

    _____

    _____

2. Is there any incongruence with either or with your own
    code?

    _____

    _____

    _____

    _____

3. Why is it important to understand any conflicts in your
    personal ethics with those of the profession or your place
    of employment?

    _____

    _____

    _____

    _____

4. How will you resolve these inconsistencies between profes-
    sional and company or your personal ethics? What will you
    do if you experience a personal or professional ethical situ-
    ation at work?

    _____

    _____

    _____

    _____

Chapter 7

Professionalism and Workplace Relationships

Student Objectives

- Understand basic workplace etiquette and professional standards
- Recognize the difference between a supervisor and a mentor, and understand their individual roles in the student's development
- Be able to identify team members in the smallest and broadest sense
- Develop an understanding of roles within the team and their fluidity

I think it's important to always keep professional and surround yourself with good people, work hard, and be nice to everyone.

—Caroline Winberg

When entering any new environment, it is important to understand the norms and mores of that social group in order to function successfully. Like ethics, there are general rules and etiquette standards that are expected in the workplace. In addition, you will have a number of people in your workplace with whom you will have official and unofficial relationships. This chapter talks about workplace etiquette and your work relationships, what is appropriate, and how to leverage your relationships for success in the workplace. In some ways professionalism is influenced by the culture of an organization. But culture, position, organizational mores are only part of the things that individuals should take into account when they are examining their level of professionalism in an organization.

Two surveys by York College of Pennsylvania provide some insight into the current impression of incoming employees.[19] Faculty and human resources professionals were interviewed regarding the current state of this generation of employees. In general, the responses indicated that students who are entering the job market are coming in with a more casual attitude than their predecessors, had misconceptions about the commitment to work that was expected, and generally exhibited a sense of entitlement. These observations included the students' lack of ability to use appropriate methods of communication, new employees feeling that they can take on more projects than they are truly equipped to handle, and their not recognizing that they have any professional faults at all.

There are general rules of socialization that I am sure you are familiar with: saying good morning, goodbye, excuse me, and on and on. These rules or manners extend to the workplace as well. In addition, within many organizations there are different social norms depending on who you are interacting with. Remember, everyone should be treated with kindness and respect, but in some organizations there is a more formal method for interaction.

In fact, it really is important to read that new employee handbook to learn the appropriate methods of communicating with your supervisor, processes that need to be followed for purchasing, practices about taking time off or even dress code. In many organizations there are rules about what information one employee can share with another. For example, it is not uncommon for companies to have strict policies on discussing your salary with other employees, your own or another's disciplinary actions, or even your professional development plan. There may even be rules regarding who you can or cannot have personal relationships with in your organization.

Speaking of relationships within the workplace, you are going to have many professional associations that may include an immediate supervisor, team members, mentor, administrative support staff, customers, and consumers. In addition, there are other people you may interact with on a daily, weekly, or monthly basis. Maybe you join a company softball team, are part of an annual hire class, or associate with a company-sponsored affinity group. Your interactions in all of these groups, settings, and company-sponsored events will be observed and evaluated by others within the organization.

Finally, in your role as employee, you may be interacting with many individuals outside of the organization to which you belong. Your contact with others is also regulated by your employer. It doesn't mean that every behavior is dictated, but it does mean that your interactions with your customers, suppliers, competitors, do reflect not only on you but on your organization as well. In addition, some companies have strict rules on receiving gifts and your responsibility to report something as simple as an invitation to a baseball game to your supervisor.

Real-Life Examples

Timothy F. Fox, PhD – Associate dean – college of engineering

Mr. Garth Brooks – Director of career services

Kyle Jackson, PhD – Professor

Ms. Laura Brady – Graduate student and teaching assistant

Mr. Michael Frazier – Graduate student and tutor

Mr. Bret Buck – Senior student and tutor

Ms. Lauren Christian – Classmate

Mr. Noah McDowell – Coffee shop manager and boss

Judy Beechfield, PhD – Student group faculty advisor

Ms. Natalie Martin – Recruiter, Company XYZ

Mr. Andrew Scarlett – Co-op/intern program manager

Mr. Tom Ericson – Co-op supervisor

Mr. Will Ronaldson – Quality engineer (your new boss)

Mr. Johann Fredrickson – COO (at your new facility)

This is the beginning of understanding social mores in the workplace. It may be different from organization to another, and even within organizations, but understanding where you are and what the norms are is the first step.

Activity(ies)

The above list is of hypothetical people who represent individuals you have probably interacted with. How do you address them? Is there a difference in the level of formality?

Provide me the name of your supervisor from a previous job. Did they directly hire you? How did you address them?

What is the dress code at your work location? Who informed you of this code? Are there deviations or leniency in the code?

You have spent the last 12 hours throwing up and you really can't make it to work. Who do you notify and how?

On your current trip to visit a supplier, you go out to dinner with some of the salespeople, and they pay the tab. Do you need to report this to your employer? They offer to take you to a professional football game, in their company suite. Can you accept? Do you need to tell anyone?

Think of a work situation that you are in or have been in. Was there a hierarchy among the team member? How was that hierarchy determined? What role did you have in the group and how did that role develop? Were you assigned the role? Did you just take it upon yourself?

Summary

I think that being a professional is mostly about respecting those around you. You are neither greater nor lesser than anyone else with whom you interact. I often have discussions with students about thanking the administrative assistant who helped them in scheduling their on-site interview and all the travel arrangements. Students may work in union environments, which can be a source of frustration for the students who love to pick up a screwdriver and fix things themselves. Knowing and understanding the culture and environment you work in are imperative to your success in those environments.

Communication is a huge part of the culture and although you may be used to texting your friends and telling them you won't be meeting up with them, that is not the appropriate way to call in sick at work, take a personal day, or schedule vacation. In addition, know the general rule for taking time off. Obviously if you have a launch of a new product on July 15, taking off the week of the fourth of July is probably not going to be an option. These are commonsense things, but it seems that sometimes new employees feel they have earned the job and the vacation time, and they should be able to take off when they want. I know you all know better!

So when you begin any new job, whether with a new company or a new group within the organization, ask, observe, and learn the social and professional norms of that group. Remember what your parents, teachers, and coaches have taught you about manners and teamwork.

Keywords

Corporate culture

Workplace communication

Formal roles

Informal roles

Hierarchy

Mentor

Supervisor

Etiquette

Supporting Materials

http://money.howstuffworks.com/business/starting-a-job/10-tips-for-effective-workplace-communication.htm

http://www.moneycrashers.com/effective-workplace-communication-skills/

Endnote

19. Bauerlein, Mark. (2015). "What Do U.S. College Graduates Lack? Professionalism." https://www.bloomberg.com/view/articles/2013-05-08/what-do-u-s-college-graduates-lack-professionalism

1. Identify your organization's policy regarding taking sick time, personal time, and vacation time.

   _____

   _____

   _____

   _____

2. Describe three factors that play a role in each of these policies.

   _____

   _____

   _____

   _____

3. How do you feel about these policies? Are they different from other places where you have been employed? Where did you find this information?

   _____

   _____

   _____

   _____

4. Repeat questions 1–3, in regards to policies for accepting gifts from vendors.

_____

_____

_____

_____

5. What is the overarching factor in handling these situations? Why is it important?

_____

_____

_____

_____

Chapter 8

Communications

What is everyone talking about?

The single biggest problem in communication is the illusion that it has taken place.

—George Bernard Shaw

The root of all conflict is communication, lack of communication, or miscommunication. Without communication we are not a very cohesive society. But there are hundreds of ways to communicate. I am sure you are familiar with the idea that you can communicate with people in a variety of ways: verbally, written, body language, facial expressions, what you don't say. Generationally, you are all familiar with using texting, Snapchat, and Instagram to communicate with your friends. You may have even expanded that to your parents, siblings, and other acquaintances. I am sure by now you have experienced that the message you are sending is not always the message the person on the other end of the text is receiving. Then there is listening and the role it plays in communication. The purpose of this chapter is to review the most appropriate and effective methods of communication and to learn some skills to be more effective in your communication.

Let's just start with the way we can communicate thoughts with others. There are handwritten notes, conversations, phone calls, voice messages, emails, Google documents, blog posts, texts, Snapchats, Instagram, Facebook, Twitter, YouTube, and sticky notes. We know these days, people generally expect to receive communications in a much quicker method than days of old: no telegrams in this day and age.

In addition to methods of communication, there is also a sense of vocabulary that you would use with different people. This is often referred to as filter. I am sure that there are words you use with your friends that you would not use with your parents, teachers, grandparents, or young nieces and nephews. We tend to talk in ways and use vocabulary that we have identified as being acceptable to and understood by our audience. No doubt in your high school English classes, your teachers coached you on writing to your audience. Well, we normally do that in daily conversation too.

Let's first talk about some general ways to communicate more effectively. Pay attention to your tone. Humans tend to add inflection and punctuation to text messages and emails that probably aren't intended. So make sure that you don't infer tone in others' electronic messages, or imply tone in yours. Thing about talking to someone face-to-face if you think they may interpret a tone, or if it is clear in their response that they did. Clearing things up earlier is always a better approach. Keep digital communications to those who really need to know. Do you really have to copy your boss on your first request to a coworker to follow up on something? And please don't "reply all" if the message is really just for one member of the group. Pay attention to who you are talking to, as that matters in how you frame your message and when you deliver it. Be concise and specific, and stay on track. When an email comes in that addresses several different projects, I don't want to have to file the details in each mailbox. Or have to search for it later. Don't stop communicating. Sometimes no news is good news, but it is important to keep your boss and team updated on the status of projects and deadlines. This will also help you just keep yourself on task as well. Sometimes the priority is the closest deadline, but letting everything go right up to the deadline can be catastrophic. Finally, if you haven't received a response, follow up.

Sometimes things get lost in the digital world. Instead of waiting weeks, give the person a call.

As you explore your discipline further and work in conjunction with a variety of organizations, you will also learn a different kind of language. There are acronyms on top of acronyms as well as shortcuts within language. You probably don't think about it much, but you are using them every day already. Organizational Behavior becomes Org. Fluid Mechanics becomes Fluids. Differential Equations becomes DiffiQ. Organic Chemistry becomes Orgo. I am sure that you are also familiar with ASAP, RSVP, and one of your generation's favorite, YOLO!

As previously mentioned, language is an important part of communication and a simple example is the language and demeanor you have with your friends and classmates as compared to that with your grandparents. There are words within your vocabulary that didn't even exist 30 years ago, including Internet, vape, frenemy, bromance, World Wide Web, crowdsourcing. I think you get the point. Our language and method of communication changes as fast as technology, it seems. So what is appropriate in the workplace? How do you know what method is the most effective form of communication?

Listening, listening, listening! Probably more important than language, audience, timeliness, and message. There is an old proverb that says, "You have two ears and one mouth; you should listen twice as much as you speak." Keep that in mind when communicating with others. What is it that they are really asking? Do they understand clearly the message that you are sending? There are several techniques for improving your listening skills that will certainly also enhance your communication skills. First, paraphrase what the other person has just told you. This confirms to them that you received the message and allows them to clarify any points that were misunderstood. For your own benefit, repeat what has been said. Repetition is a great memory tool and it will help you to remember what was said. Finally, inquire further for details or missing information. You want to make sure that you have the whole picture of what is being explained. Imagine that you are asking someone for directions. Just one missing step and you could be completely lost. Whether you are driving around a city or solving a complex equation, the details matter.

Real-Life Examples

Acronyms
YOLO
RSVP
EE
CompSci
SAP
MLP
WWW
TTYL
BFF
LMK

Words
On fleek
Hashtag
Internet
Jeggings
Locavore
Purple State
Upcycle

Activity(ies)

Just for fun, without using Google, define the acronyms and the words above.

Tell me in both methodology and wording how you would inform your supervisor that you were having car trouble and would be late for work.

You clearly have the flu and don't feel well enough to go to work today. Give me both the methodology and wording you would use to inform work. Who would you tell?

You are having problems completing your project within the time frame that you established with your team. How would you communicate this? Who would you tell?

Your boss asks you to prepare a summary of your internship to share with the company president. What do you include? How would you deliver it?

Your internship advisor from your university asks you to share information about your summer work experience. What would that report look like?

You are talking to your friends about your summer. How do you tell them and what do you include?

You have been working on a project all semester and it is time to pass it on to the next intern. Tell me what you have done to prepare for this day and how you will be sure that the next intern understands the project and project goals.

Create your résumé description of your internship.

Summary

Communication is the most important aspect of every relationship you will ever have. When discussing difficult situations it is important to remain calm and keep emotions out of the conversation. In many cases there are times when a deadline has been missed or something was done in the wrong manner. If this happens, remember to focus not on HOW you got there, but WHAT you can do to fix it. Think about how you move forward! Focusing on the mistakes in the heat of the moment is counterproductive. Even if you as the new kid made a mistake, come clean and focus on what you can do to fix it.

There is certainly not enough room in this workbook to discuss all the methods of communication within the workplace. The best advice I can give you is to observe what is being said, especially between your supervisor and senior staff at your organization. In general, it is better to be conservative in your methods. As a professional, you will be responsible for documenting your work and the company will probably have some forms and standards that they expect you to follow. If in doubt ask! That is what supervisors, mentors, and colleagues are for.

Keywords

Communication

Acronyms

Verbal communication

Technical reports

Internal audience

External audience

Supporting Materials

http://www.forbes.com/sites/amyanderson/2013/05/28/successful-business-communication-it-starts-at-the-beginning/

http://smallbusiness.chron.com/7-cs-effective-business-communication-114.html

http://www.forbes.com/sites/susanadams/2013/11/19/how-to-communicate-effectively-at-work-3/

1. Please learn the accepted forms of communication within this organization for reporting and requesting time off, for documenting professional work, and for creating reports for internal and external constituents.

_____

_____

_____

_____

2. Where would you look and where did you find examples of appropriate work-related communication documents?

_____

_____

_____

_____

3. What specific areas have you identified that you need to work on in professional communication? How are you planning to do that?

_____

_____

_____

_____

4. How will you measure progress or success on this particular skill set?

_____

_____

_____

_____

5. Did you completely achieve this goal? If so, how? If not, what still needs to be done?

_____

_____

_____

_____

Chapter 9

Why do I need to understand economics? I have no budget.

Student Objectives

- Understand that time is money, and what that means in a for-profit organization
- Understand and perform a cost-benefit analysis for a project
- Understand the concept of Economic Equivalence and the role it plays in business
- Develop an awareness of the financial impact of workplace decisions

Economics is everywhere, and understanding economics can help you make better decisions and lead a happier life.

—Tyler Cowen

We all want to be a part of the latest and the greatest thing since sliced bread, Nintendo, Wii, and Snapchat. It is no secret that if you have all the money in the world, you can design and build some really cool stuff. But there is a fine balance between what something costs to design and build, what a consumer will pay for it, and what the price should be so enough people buy it to make it profitable!

The world runs on money. We need money to design, manufacture, market, sell, and maintain a product. Whether we are talking about a car, a drug, a phone app, or a service concept, there is a cost associated with creating and producing the product or service, maintaining quality control, and meeting the needs of the customer. It is important for you to know whether you are creating the newest product or are somewhere in the process of delivering that product to the customer, and that you are aware of the balance between cost and outcome.

Theoretically speaking, we want to make sure that the cost to design, develop, and produce a product is in line with what the market will tolerate in terms of the price to the public. This price should ultimately cover all of the design, development, and production costs as well as an adequate profit for the organization.

This is just how business is—it doesn't matter whether you are making lemonade for the neighborhood kids or creating a rocket ship that will go to the moon, you have to consider the costs involved and the return on your investment. Now for lemonade, we all know your mom bought the sugar, the lemons, and the water. So you mixed it together and sold it for a quarter a cup (which your mom also paid for), so *your* profit per cup is $0.25. I would say that is an awesome return on your investment. The rocket ship of course is an easy billion, so let's just use that as our mark, $1,000,000,000. What is your return on that investment? Invention of Memory foam and selling it for a cool $5 million? Nike Air soles as a spin-off of space suits, resulting in, let's say, $4,000,000. I could go on with things like invisible braces, the game controller joystick, cordless tools, solar panels; all of which made huge profits in the down-to-earth human market. And that doesn't even count the groundbreaking research in the field of astrophysics—priceless!

Clearly the investment for the rocket paid dividends to the investor. Are there things you can think of that might not have proven so profitable? I am having trouble coming up with one, but let's use the DeLorean as an example. Millions were invested by some seriously famous and well-connected people, but the cost of the car itself, a market that wasn't prepared for the product, and a recession all led to a concept that wasn't cost effective to produce.

Real-life Examples:

47 Ronin

Paranormal activity   Viagra

Facebook   MySpace

The DeLorean   The Flying Saucer camera

Nitrous oxide   Wearable parachute

Virtual boy   Shakeweight

The electric pen   Pet Rock

Hoverboard   Car Cane

Activity(ies)

Have you ever thought of a new product or service? What was it? If not, think of something you might be interested in doing now? What kind of product or service is it? Dream big!

What would it take to get this product or service to market? Think of all the costs that could be associated with concept to market. I am not looking for numbers here, but the processes, materials, resources, etc., that will be required.

Find an example of a cost-analysis worksheet or process for a product in your industry. Are there factors discussed that you had not thought about? Are there things that you think should be considered but aren't?

Looking at one of the real-life examples above, what do you think could or should have been done differently, if anything, for a successful project launch? What were the factors that contributed to their success or failure?

Summary

The point of this chapter is that you can have the greatest idea in the world, which could change society, but if you don't take the time to do a cost analysis of the product, you will likely not be successful. On the other hand, if you do the homework upfront and look at all of the factors that may make for a successful product, you can get a huge return on your investment for a seemingly simple concept.

For many students and professionals, this process is tedious, time consuming, and frustrating. It is, however, essential to the successful launch of a new product or service. As part of the whole picture, you need to determine whether: there is a need for the product; people will understand what you are trying to sell; and if the market is already saturated with products that can do the same thing. In addition, I would urge you to look beyond the original concept. What products would follow? Is there a need for them? What is the viability of those projects? Being a one-hit wonder can make you some money, but will you be able to sustain yourself on that income, support other concepts and ventures, and get more money coming in?

Keywords

Economics

Budget

Economy of scale

Cost analysis

Return on investment (ROI)

Supporting Materials

https://www.projectsmart.co.uk/creating-a-project-budget-what-you-need-to-know.php

https://www.liquidplanner.com/blog/7-ways-create-budget-project/

http://www.techrepublic.com/article/creating-your-project-budget-where-to-begin/

1. Create a conceptual product/service/concept. Tell us about it.

   _____

   _____

   _____

   _____

2. Describe the factors that need to be considered before taking this product to market. Resources, resources, resources?

   _____

   _____

   _____

   _____

3. What obstacles do you see in preventing the launch of this product? Time, money, materials?

   _____

   _____

   _____

   _____

4. What steps can you take to mitigate these obstacles? Show me your creativity!

_____

_____

_____

_____

5. How would you determine product success? How many do you have to sell? What needs to happen for you to say, YES I DID IT!

_____

_____

_____

_____

Chapter 10

I have managed my life, I can manage a project!

Student Objectives

- Understand the phases of project management and be able to contribute to each phase
- Preview a variety of project monitoring and management tools
- Develop a standard approach to project management and planning
- Be aware of supply chain and other factors that may affect plan execution

Even if you are on the right track, you will get run over if you just sit there!

—Will Rogers

I imagine that some people reading this chapter will be a little confused by the combination of project management and organizational skills. I think, however, that organization is the key to productivity, both your own and that of your team. As a supervisor, having someone on my team who is organized and focused is a huge bonus for me. I am organized, in my head, but maybe not on my desk, or not in a way that allows others to see the process that I have going on. That is great for me; I am primarily autonomous in my job, and I have others who I work with who are super task oriented and focused. I am also pretty far up the food chain in my organization. I say that because I would argue that a younger me was much more task oriented, much more organized in what I had to do and by when I had to do it, and how much time and how many resources it would take to accomplish those goals. This provided me not only with the knowledge and experience to now wing it, but also showed my supervisors and teammates that I was on the ball, I could get things done. I could help everyone else stay on track. These are all skills that a supervisor is going to pay attention to when they are looking to reward or promote, or they have a super opportunity for someone! There is an old saying, "If you want something done, give it to the busiest person." As we talk about this, please don't confuse looking busy with being productive. I am talking about being productive. There is another saying, "Don't work hard, work smart!" I want to see people who are productive, not just running around doing things for the sake of doing things.

Ok, so let's break down these two concepts: Project management and organizational skills. **Project management** is the application of processes, methods, knowledge, skills, and experience to achieve the **project** objectives. A **project** is a unique, transient endeavor, undertaken to achieve planned objectives, which could be **defined** in terms of outputs, outcomes, or benefits.[21] **Organizational skills** refers to the ability to use your time, energy, resources, etc., in an effective way so that you achieve the things you want to achieve. Self-discipline and **organizational skills** are crucial to success in any profession.[22] Translated project management is the task, organizational skills are the tool.

Project management is actually a big business these days: you can get a certificate, a diploma, or a degree in project management. As we like to say in our office, "This isn't brain surgery!" Right, it is having a particular goal or outcome or objective in mind, and how to proceed to achieve that outcome. Now if it is just you, say, writing a workbook for students, you have a plan. Sure you may have a publisher breathing down your neck with some deadlines, but okay, that is part of your objective: have this book completed by a certain date. You may also know that you want this workbook to include certain topics and specific activities to teach the topics, and that, ultimately, the people using the book will gain something from it! But it is just you, writing a book. Now let's say it is you and a few others writing a chapter of a mystery novel. It is a game you may have all played before. One person starts the story and then each person needs to add to the story with one or two sentences as you go around the room. You may not have a particular end in mind for the story, but you know by time you get around the circle, there needs to be an ending. So you have an individual role, as does everyone in the room, for a specific outcome. Project management is that on a grand scale, but know that one person in the room is going to check for grammar, another for spelling, a third for consistency in the details, a fourth for compliance with publisher regulations and restrictions. They contribute to the project as a whole, but they also have a particular skill set or component of the project that is their primary responsibility. Now we know that you can't have someone check for typos if the document isn't written yet! That you can't make sure you are in compliance if you don't know the rules. I can't write my part until the part before mine is done. Things need to be done independently and simultaneously. The process that keeps all that working smoothly is project management.

Organizational skills are the tools and processes that keep you on track in achieving your goals: Having a process of knowing what needs to be done and by when, a place or frame of reference for where you can get the resources you need to complete your project, and a timeline or reminder system to make sure tasks are completed as needed. Most of us develop a process that works for us. As a college student you probably already have a system in place for when homework is due; what activities you plan on attending; when you have blocked off time for the gym, class, and doing homework. These are organizational skills. You may think that you haven't really developed these. I would argue that if you are a successful student in even a modest sense, you have some kind of process in place. Figure out what it is and what works for you. Are you more successful if you have a part-time job? Get your workout in early in the morning? Schedule time for yoga or church or some form of personal reflection? How can these processes and skill sets help you in the workplace and help to identify you as the key person the team leader goes to in order to make sure that things get done?

Activity(ies)

Identify some methods that you currently use to keep yourself organized and on track.

Do you often find yourself in a situation where you forgot to do something? Why is that? Or why not?

Describe your current organizational style to someone who is completely unfamiliar with the topic.

Do you use a particular tool to keep you on track? Electronic, paper, sticky notes?

Why do you think that does or doesn't work for you? Could or would it work on a larger scale with money and your job on the line?

What experience have you had with project management?

Are you familiar with any project management tools?

Locate a project management resource that fits your style. Why do you like this one?

Give me an example of a project that you have been a part of. What role did you play? Was the project successful? What kept it from being a success? What could have made it better?

Summary

There is no right answer or method for either project management or learning or using organizational skills. You need to find something that works for you. Be aware that many organizations use software or have a standard operating procedure for project management. It is important that you become familiar with the concept and be flexible enough to adapt to a given package. I believe the best way to do that is to just apply the general project management principles to everyday projects that you participate in. In addition, knowing from an organizational perspective what does and doesn't work for you is a tremendous step in integrating your style with that of your organization.

Keywords

Project management
Organizational skills

Supporting Materials

https://www.entrepreneur.com/article/242359
http://www.gvtc.org/contents/organization.pdf

Endnotes

21. https://www.apm.org.uk/WhatIsPM

22. http://dictionary.cambridge.org/us/dictionary/english/organizational-skills

1. Identify a product, service, goal, or objective that will
    require multiple aspects for the achievement of the final
    outcome—something that would require project manage-
    ment and organizations skills. (This can be something you
    are currently working on or something that you have done
    in the past.)

    _____

    _____

    _____

    _____

2. Did you use any project management tools for the execu-
    tion of this project? If so, which one(s)? How did it work?
    Did the whole team participate? What was the general
    response to the tool? If you didn't use a project manage-
    ment tool for this project, do you think it would have
    helped? If so, how? If not, why not?

    _____

    _____

    _____

    _____

3. Identify any weaknesses you may have in your organizational skills toolbox. What do you have trouble with? What don't you know how to do? What issues have prevented you from keeping on track in the past?

_____

_____

_____

_____

4. Set some realistic goals to learn a project management method that will keep you on track. What, when, and why?

_____

_____

_____

_____

5. Create a plan to enhance your organizational skills. Where can you get assistance in developing these skills?

_____

_____

_____

_____

Chapter 11

Yeah, what is this whole work-life balance thing?

- Understand the concept of work–life balance
- Recognize their own work–life balance needs
- Identify resources and activities to maintain that balance
- Identify and manage stressors

I think a good life–work balance is important, and that's even more important in some cases on the space station.

—Scott Kelly

There is a long history of people's identity being tied up to their work, their professions, their creations. The success or failure of this identity is linked directly and completely to the success or failure of the work or creations. This doesn't always end well. We could take some drastic examples of successful people who at the end of their professional career failed to thrive.

A good friend of mine told me of a professional sports team that has been hugely successful, winning six national championships. The first four of these were closely bundled and there were twenty-six men who were part of those four championship runs. Of those, eighteen were identified as all-stars/pro-bowlers and seven are in the Hall of Fame. This is an amazing record of success. We all know that playing a professional sport is usually a short-term proposition; careers as an active participant usually come to an end within ten years. Twenty-six highly successful athletes, and after their professional career was over, twelve were homeless for a while. My friend's observation was that their lives were wrapped up in their identity as a superstar athlete and when that went away, they had nothing.

So to me, work–life balance is more than just making sure you schedule time for the gym, dates with your significant other, or Sunday dinner with your parents. It is about balancing your energies, emotions, activities, successes, and failures. In this chapter we are going to explore some ways not just to balance your schedule so that you don't get burned out on the job, but also to balance your energy and efforts, to spread your successes outside of your work, so you will always have a purpose and find meaning in life.

Activity(ies)

Does your company have a policy on work–life balance? A resource center? Anything that you think would contribute to assisting employees in creating a balanced life? Is this a priority for your organization? If not, why do you think it isn't?

Do you think the university assists students in creating a work–life balance? How? If not, why do you think it doesn't?

Should the responsibility of work–life balance lie with the organization or the individual? Why? Explain the role that each should play.

Summary

I don't think we are likely to have a perfect circle of work–life balance. Like all of the things in your life, some are going to demand more energy at some points than at others. These peaks of energy will ebb and flow among the things that you determine to be important in your life. This is a very personal concept. For some people family will always come first, but what that looks like might be different for the primary breadwinner in the family than for the primary caregiver in the family. Sometimes you have to be both, and you need to be okay in knowing that working overtime is giving you money to send your kids to college or summer camp. Or you need to understand that your sacrifice of working 60+ hours a week will be rewarded when you take those three weeks off to travel through India. Again, balance isn't about time, necessarily. It is about putting your energies and efforts into things that are a priority for you. It is personal and different for everyone. Don't allow anyone else's concept of balance interfere with what your priorities are. And remember what we talked about in the beginning of this chapter: create ways to be successful in the things that are important to you and spread your successes around and you will find your balance.

Keywords

Work–life balance

Success

Breadwinner

Caregiver

Supporting Materials

https://www.youtube.com/watch?v=fM7UQakOzxM

https://www.youtube.com/watch?v=jdpIKXLLYYM

Use the work–life balance wheel exercise available on MindTools.com. Complete the wheel and the exercises throughout the page.

What did you learn? What areas of your life do you need to work on? How do you think this will change in the next five years, ten years? Why is that important?

_____

_____

_____

_____

_____

_____

_____

_____

_____

_____

_____

_____

Chapter 12

Make it so! Your future looks bright!

Student Objectives

- Begin to identify their short- and long-term personal and professional goals
- Classify and prioritize these goals
- Recognize the steps that need to be taken to achieve these goals
- Develop a plan for achieving these goals
- Understand that these goals may change but the skill set is needed to reset the process along the way

Only you can control your future.

—Dr. Seuss

Excuse the *Star* **Trek** reference, but I happen to like Jean-Luc Picard. I am pretty sure that he is confident in the crew achieving a particular goal when he utters those famous words, "Make it so"! I don't have to tell you that time is short for you to have a plan, a path, some goals, and some destinations in mind. I know you had goals when you started your journey at this institution. How have those goals changed? Did you change your major? Your career destination? Did your priorities change? I think the journey of this workbook should have given you some insight into turning your college major into a career in something that you love and will allow you to also focus on the other important things in your life.

As an academic I often worry about the incongruent nature of the stated mission of institutions of higher education and the intent and outcomes of those students who pass through our doors. We want you to come here and learn to be intelligent, active, contributing members of society. You want to come and learn what you need to learn to get a job you enjoy and that pays the bills. Now that may be pretty simplistic, but I think it provides you with a picture of my concerns. I think we can do both, and I hope I have given you some of the skills that will get you to that place and will carry you through the rest of your life. These aren't just exercises for the here and now. You can continue to use them as you move from job to job, as you deal with relationships in your personal life, as you have kids and as your parents get old.

I also hope at this point in our relationship, you have moved past the perceived busywork of this workbook. I am optimistic that you have been able to really take the exercises and learn a little about yourself as a student, an employee, a contributing member of society, and a person. You have value and worth, and if you ever doubt that, look back to where you began; you are not in the same place. As humans, there is no such thing as going backward, we can't unlearn lessons. Sure occasionally we forget them and have to be reminded, but we don't unlearn. We also have moved along the path, maybe in a different direction than the one we first started, but we still move. The concept of reincarnation is that our souls come back to relearn lessons that we missed on our previous visits. You don't need to come back just to relearn a lesson.

The tools shared in this book can be used over and over again as you find yourself in different settings. Communication rules, patterns, and styles may change. You are going to need to learn to talk to your kids, or those new young people who are hired in your organization. You are going to change companies, get a promotion, or move to another state; all those events are opportunities to reevaluate your goals, take measure of your skill sets, and consider your mind-set and your mindfulness. This goes back to the concept of lifelong learning. Just because you achieve a goal doesn't mean that you stop—to keep yourself happy, motivated, and confident, you set another goal, and on and on!

There are no real-life examples in this chapter, there is only you! Think about goals you have set in your life, from tying your shoes to riding a bike to walking home from grade school without your mom or dad or older sibling; making the team, be it basketball, soccer, cheer, or debate; winning a school election; building your first computer from scratch; making your first investment in the stock market; getting into college, surviving your freshman roommate, and passing that weeder course in your major. You might not have thought of them as goals at the time, but that's what they were and you accomplished them, or something similar. You have been achieving your whole life and you have been making choices to achieve—you just weren't thinking that way. But now you are college educated, career prepared, and ready to adult! The following resources are to help you now and as you go forward into the real world.

Activity(ies)

Tell me the first time you set you remember setting your sights on a goal. What was it and what did you have to do to achieve it?

Tell me when someone in your life recognized that you had set a goal. What was their response and how did that make you feel?

Have you ever been derailed on a particular goal? Not get admitted to your first college choice? Not become student body president? Not make the varsity football team? What was your response after you got over the initial shock and disappointment?

If you have never been derailed on a goal, why do you think that is?

Identify a nonacademic-, nonwork-related goal you have for your life that you hope to attain in the next five years. Ten years. What has to happen for you to achieve those goals? How will you feel if you get derailed in the process?

Summary

Ah the end is near; I have thoroughly enjoyed this journey with you! I have! The fact is I have been taking my own journey along with you. Yes I am well into my professional career. You can call me seasoned or mature, but I am still learning and dreaming, and shooting for the stars. Why, you ask? Well because I have found a job that I love—nay, a career that I love—that allows me to continue to grow, hopefully have a positive impact on those who I interact with, and, frankly, pays the bills! What more could I ask for? I have been able to travel the world, provide for those I love, and generally love coming to work. Don't get me wrong— I have days that I don't love. Life gets in the way of work and work gets in the way of life! But they also complement each other and that is a true meaning of work–life balance. I want to continue to love my life, so I occasionally reevaluate it along the way. I am going to leave you with a particular resource that I recently found that I am excited about using with students, with myself, and with my friends. In its most simplistic form, it is value identification and then using a particular process to see all the factors that go into supporting that value within your life. You can use it as a goal achievement process as well. The concept is called Mind Mapping or Mind Maps.

Mind Mapping allows you to identify and focus on a particular value or goal and then see the factors or topics that go along with and support that value or goal.

Keywords

Mind mapping

Goals

Values

Supporting Materials

http://www.studygs.net/mapping/exercise2.htm

https://www.mindtools.com/pages/article/newISS_01.htm

https://www.mindmeister.com/723328623?new=1

Worksheet

Your final assignment for this workbook is to watch this video on mind mapping. What do you think of this concept? Is it something you have done before? How did you feel about it then?

_____

_____

_____

_____

Now, access this mind-mapping exercise and create a mind map for a value or goal that you have in your life. It can be outlandish (saving your first million dollars) or something practical for your current life situation (finishing college without getting in more debt).

_____

_____

_____

What do you think about this process? Did it bring any new light to your goals? Your path toward your goals?

_____

_____

_____

_____